To Jarmila

Love,

The Magee's

Mushrooms
A
Separate Kingdom

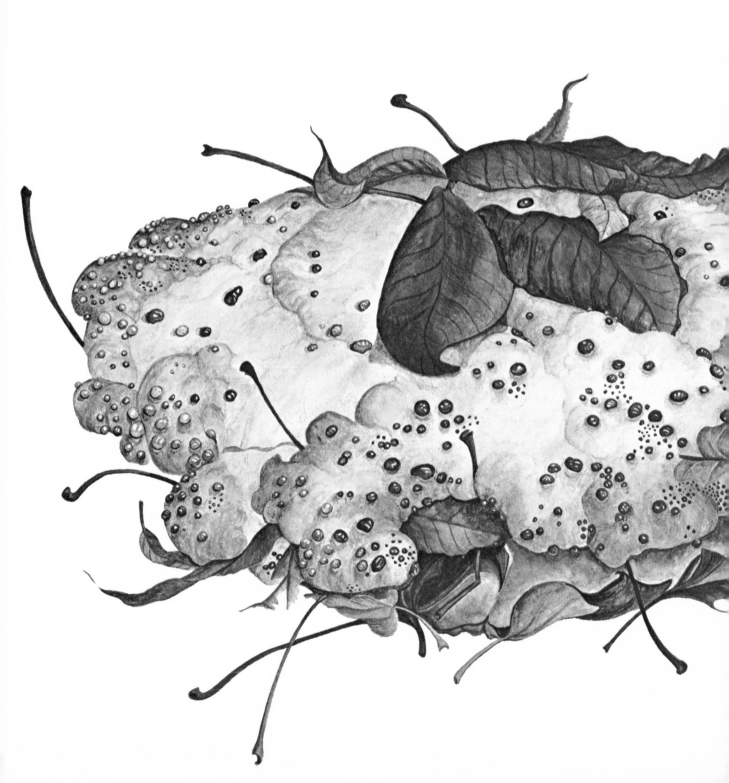

Mushrooms

A Separate Kingdom

Illustrations and calligraphy by
Loni Parker

Text by
David T. Jenkins

Oxmoor House, Inc. · Birmingham

Eugene Butler   Chairman of the Board
Emory Cunningham   President and Publisher
Vernon Owens, Jr.,   Senior Executive Vice President

Conceived, edited and published by Oxmoor House, Inc., under
the direction of:

Don Logan   Vice President and General Manager
Gary McCalla   Editor, *Southern Living*®
John Logue   Editor-in-Chief
Jerry Higdon   Production Manager
Mary Jean Haddin   Copy Chief

MUSHROOMS: A SEPARATE KINGDOM

Editor: Karen Phillips Irons
Designer: Viola Andrycich

Library of Congress Catalog Number: 79-88459
ISBN: 0-8487-0501-7
Manufactured in the United States of America
First Printing

Each mushroom has been painted in its actual size and is
accurately represented. However, The Progressive Farmer
Company does not intend that this book be used as a guide
to edible mushrooms.

Contents

This world, as a glorious apartment of the boundless palace of the sovereign Creator, is furnished with an infinite variety of animated scenes, inexpressibly beautiful and pleasing, equally free to the inspection and enjoyment of all his creatures.

TRAVELS by William Bartram
The Beehive Press, Savannah, Georgia
Copyright© 1973
Facsimile Edition (of 1792 Edition)

Preface

When I was a child in postwar Austria, my father, Alfred Kala, taught me to recognize many edible mushrooms. During these years, this knowledge became very valuable. At first we needed every mushroom, except the poisonous, for food. But as conditions improved, we narrowed our edible list until we collected only the two most delectable ones, Boletus edulis and Cantharellus cibarius.

Today, my husband, our two daughters, and I live in the center of 40 wooded acres in Alabama. One particularly wet summer my daily walks in the woods revealed a multitude of mushrooms I had never seen. Since I had enjoyed collecting and eating wild Austrian mushrooms, I decided this would be a good time to learn about the fungi of the South.

I began painting mushrooms so that each one could be accurately identified later. What started as a gourmet's search for wild delicacies quickly developed into full-fledged enchantment with the colors and shapes of fungi. I realized that in my eagerness as a child to fill my basket with edible mushrooms, I had neglected the beauty of many others. By summer's end, I had painted 95 mushrooms from our woods.

Not until last summer, however, did the idea of publishing a book of my mushroom paintings start to become a reality. As I thought about it, I wondered if my lifelong fascination with calligraphy could also be included. Through a conversation with friends, I was encouraged to make actual plans for a book containing both my paintings and my calligraphy. Within a month, I had a meeting with David Jenkins, who became the author, and Oxmoor House agreed to publish the work.

When I confronted my family with my decision to write this book, they were naturally very excited. Little did they know what they were getting into! I started work at one end of our dining room table. Gradually, several chairs were stacked with boxes used to prop up mushrooms; then I added a dictionary, lettering and painting supplies, seedpods, and miscellaneous items. Also, I installed an aquarium so that various creatures could have their portraits painted in comfort. Soon there was no place to eat. Sometimes I longed for a quiet cloister like those where the monks of the fifteenth century produced their manuscripts. (My family may well have wished me there, too.)

But those were minor inconveniences in the creation of this book, a process which has been extremely gratifying. I would like to thank all the people who, in one way or another, made it possible.

Loni Parker

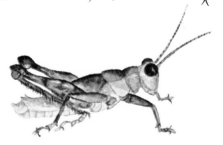

To my Family

The natural history of the

Mushroom

The mushroom is unique ~ a living organism that is neither plant nor animal. It has no seed or root. It seems to spring full grown from the ground after rain. It lives in a "separate kingdom."

Mushrooms fascinated the ancients and piqued their sense of logic. When they saw mushrooms spring up after rain~with no apparent time for genesis or growth~the ancients called them "a callosity of the earth," "earthy excrescences,"and "the evil ferment of the earth." They assembled elaborate syllogisms to explain the mushroom's apparent contradictions and lack of cause. Plutarch assembled this parallelism about truffles, a type of mushroom: During thunderstorms, flame comes from soft vapors. Deafening noises come from soft clouds. Why then, if two such violent forces could issue from softness, should not violent lightning, striking the ground, cause soft truffles?

Pliny, the Greek naturalist, also attempted to explain the mushroom mystery: "The origin of mushrooms is the slime and souring juices of moist earth, or frequently the root of acorn-bearing trees; at first it is flimsier than froth, then it grows substantial like parchment, and then the mushroom is born."

To the ancients the mushroom was an affront to logic: an effect without a cause, a seeming plant without a root that often sought darkness instead of light. Today, of course, we know that it is not the spectacular elements of the thunderstorm, but gentle rain, that seems to call the mushroom out of the earth. As for its cause: instead of seeds, it produces tiny reproductive structures called spores. These spores are produced on the underside of the cap be-

tween the gills. Soon after a mushroom develops to maturity, the spores fall from between the gills and are blown away by the wind. If any of the spores should land where the environmental conditions are appropriate (i.e., high moisture and nutrient content), germination and growth could occur.

A plant seed holds within it the primordial parts of the adult plant: root, stem, and leaves. Most plant parts, examined under a microscope, reveal characteristically individual, roundish cells. But the mushroom has innumerable, tiny, threadlike filaments referred to as hyphae or mycelia. These hyphae are frequently differentiated (that is, structurally different), and compactly arranged into various structures such as the umbrellalike cap, the radiating, bladelike gills, and the supporting stem.

When the spore has found a suitable place, growth begins with tiny hyphal filaments emerging from the spore. The hyphae then branch and grow in all directions, meandering among the soil particles.

Fortunately, all spores produced by mushrooms do not germinate and grow to maturity. It has been estimated that the puffball, Calvatia gigantea, produces approximately 7,000,000,000,000 spores in one fruit body that weighs only ½ pound. If each of these spores were to germinate, grow, and produce an equally large fruit body, their combined mass would be approximately 800 times the size of the planet earth.

The germinating hyphae are different from those found within a mature mushroom in that they show little differentiation and are not organized into specific structures. However, since this spore germination and subsequent growth (called a mycelium) take place beneath the surface of the soil, they go completely unnoticed. How does this fungus growth relate to the development of a mushroom?

As an apple is to an apple tree, similarly is a mushroom to this underground mycelium. These subterranean hyphae are, in actuality, the main body of the fungus, which ultimately produces a characteristic mushroom. This mushroom production, however, is usually not as consistent as is the production of apples on an apple tree. The conditions that stimulate mushroom production are not completely known, but abundant moisture and warm temperatures are frequently important.

The first sign of mushroom growth is the production of microscopic tufts of hyphae which continue to increase in size and become densely compacted. With this increase come the differentiation of the hyphae and the formation of the various mushroom parts. When the development of this diminutive mushroom is complete, we refer to the entire structure as a "mushroom button."

5

This "button" may be less than ½ inch in diameter. How does this tiny mushroom, which may still be buried beneath the surface of the soil, become the large mushroom that we recognize? Have you forgotten rain, noted by the ancients?

It is certainly not uncommon to go into your yard following a heavy rain and find numerous mushrooms that were not there before the rain. Or were they? Over 90 percent of the composition of a mature mushroom is water, obtained through rapid absorption by the hyphae. The increase in size from a "mushroom button" to a mature mushroom results from this absorption of water. Therefore, although the mushrooms seem to have sprung up from nothing, following a rain, we now know that the mushroom has been growing for several days, and that what we see is the rapid enlargement of the mushroom due to the absorption of water. Most mature mushrooms last for only a few days, whereas the underground part of the fungus may last for years.

Green plants produce their food by a process called photosynthesis, which requires the green pigment chlorophyll, water, carbon dioxide, certain minerals, and energy from the sun. This process takes place in the leaves of the plant with the water and minerals being taken in through the roots. Theophrastus, a student of the Greek philosopher Aristotle, recognized that a mushroom does not have a root, stem, branch, bud, leaf,

6

flower, or fruit. Since mushrooms do not have leaves or roots, they are incapable of such a process.

Since mushrooms do not produce their own food, they must obtain it from other living organisms or decaying material. As the mushroom mycelium ramifies through the soil, it, by chance, comes into contact with dead materials. Some of these materials are simple enough so that they can be absorbed directly into the hyphae. More complex materials must be broken down into simpler materials by chemicals that are released from the mycelium. These materials can then be absorbed into the hyphae and used by the fungus to continue growing. This process, decay, is the fungi's contribution to the earth's biological cycles. Without fungi, biological wastes would build up very rapidly, eventually choking out all other life.

There are sources of organic matter, other than that found decaying in the ground, providing a source of nutrition for the fungi. Maybe you've seen mushrooms growing on the wooden rail on your patio, on a dead tree standing in the forest, on dung lying in a pasture, or on a railroad tie. There are few organic substances that, given proper moisture and warm temperatures, cannot be attacked by

some fungus. Quite frequently the type of nutrient materials available will determine the types of mushrooms that will grow there. This is why you may find the same type of mushrooms growing in the same place year after year.

Some mushrooms obtain their nutrition by growing in association with other living organisms. Many have developed specific growth relationships to certain plants: the mycelium of the mushroom may be connected to the roots of a certain plant. Through this relationship, called mycorrhizae, an exchange of nutrient materials takes place. Because of these specific relationships, you frequently find certain mushrooms only growing near certain trees. They may also develop from mycelia which permeate parts of the tree, absorbing nutrient materials produced by the tree. While some mushrooms grow on trees without noticeable damage to the tree, others, stealing life-supporting

materials, eventually destroy the tree. Certain of the shelf fungi (in particular, the species of the genus Fomes) cause very destructive wood rots. One mushroom, Armillariella mellea, considered a good edible by most people, produces a serious disease that is called "shoestring root rot."

We generally associate mushroom growth with the warm, moist conditions and abundance of nutrients found in forested areas. But not all mushrooms grow in forests. Many can be seen growing in lawns, pastures, meadows, or farmland. Finding enough moisture and adequate nutrients, mushrooms grow well almost anywhere.

Much information has been accumulated concerning mushroom structure, growth, reproduction, and habitats. Professional mycologists (those who study fungi) are continually involved in research projects in an attempt to learn more about

9

this strange separate kingdom of living organisms. But many mysteries remain.

Pliny said, "Now whether this imperfection of the earth, for it cannot be said to be anything else, grows, or whether it has at once assumed its full globular size, whether it lives or not, are matters which I think cannot be easily understood."

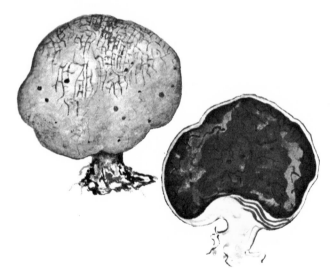

The edible
and the poisonous

If a friend suggested that it would be fun to go into the forest and collect some wild mushrooms to eat, how would you react? You would probably shudder in horror, responding that you do not know how to separate the edible from the poisonous varieties and probably thinking that most mushrooms are poisonous anyway.

More than likely, your reasons for not collecting the mushrooms would be based more on fantasy and misconception than fact. Nevertheless, you would be wise not to rush out and collect mushrooms that you cannot accurately identify.

Are most mushrooms poisonous? Certainly not. Relatively few mushrooms possess dangerous toxins. Some of the most poisonous varieties are quite common, however. Several genera contain toxic varieties. Probably the genus that is most frequently associated with poisonings is Amanita. The "Death Cap," Amanita phalloides, and the "Destroying Angel," Amanita virosa, have long been known for their toxic potential.

Both of the above mushrooms are found in the United States. The "Death Cap," although relatively rare, has been collected in the northeastern and western states. The "Destroying Angel" is common in many more states. In the southeastern states several common varieties (such as Amanita virosa and Amanita bi-

15

sporigera, both solid white) contain deadly toxins.

In Europe, where mushroom foraging is very common, a large majority of all deaths related to mushroom poisoning are caused by Amanita phalloides. One of the most tragic incidents involving this mushroom occurred in 1918 in Poznan, Poland. Thirty-one school children died from eating a mushroom dish prepared at their school.

One reason that over 90 percent of fatal mushroom poisonings result from consuming members of this mushroom group is the period of 6 to 24 hours before the onset of symptoms. These include sharp, colicky abdominal pains, nausea, vomiting, and water diarrhea. Apparent recovery may occur. Then after the second day abdominal pains reoccur, and the victim has jaundice, renal dysfunction, convulsions, and coma. Death usually results. The treatment is complex and not guaranteed to be successful.

But not all mushroom toxins are deadly. Some, such as those found in Chlorophyllum molybdites, a common lawn mushroom, will just make you very ill. Coprinus atramentarius is ordinarily a good edible mushroom. However, if alcohol is consumed following the meal, even up to four or five days later, characteristic reactions will follow. These include a hot flushing of the face and neck, a metallic taste in the mouth, a tingling sensation in the extremities, a rapid heart beat, and vomiting and nausea. Recovery is spontaneous in 2 to 4 hours.

You might find it hard to believe that some people eat toxic mushrooms on purpose, but the practice is not uncommon. These mushrooms are not those that will always make you sick, but those that will make you "high." The toxins of several varieties of mushrooms fall under the popular heading of recreational drugs. These include species of such genera as Amanita, Psilocybe, Panaeolus, and Conocybe. The two genera most frequently associated with the "highs" are Amanita and Psilocybe.

The hallucinogenic members of Psilocybe are quite common in the United States, particularly in the southeastern and northwestern states. Frequently, after good rains, you can go into many cow pastures and find specimens growing on cow dung. However, there are simple ways that these mushrooms can be grown in the home. Because they are easy to collect and no known deaths have occured from eating these mushrooms, they have become quite popular. However, this is in no way a recommendation that you try these mushroom varieties because they could be quite hazardous to your health.

The popularity of the effects of eating these mush-

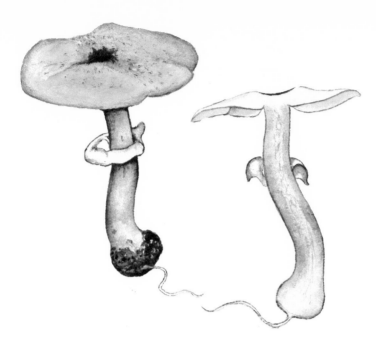

rooms was stimulated by several publications by R. G. Wasson, in which he studied the use of these mush rooms by the Mexican Indians. The Aztec name given to these mushrooms was "teonancatl," the flesh of the god. The mushrooms seemed to be used primarily in the Aztec religious ceremonies. One account of their use is given by a Spanish friar, Bernardino de Sahagun:"The first thing which they ate at the gathering was small, black mushrooms which they called nancatl. These are intoxicating and cause visions to be seen and even provoke sensuousness. They ate these before dawn, and they also drank chocolate before daylight. They ate these little mushrooms with honey, and when they began to be excited by them, they began to dance, some singing, others weeping, for they were already intoxicated by the mushrooms. Some did not want to sing but sat down in their quarters and remained there as if in a meditative mood. Some saw themselves dying in a vision and wept; others saw themselves being eaten by a wild beast; others imagined that they

18

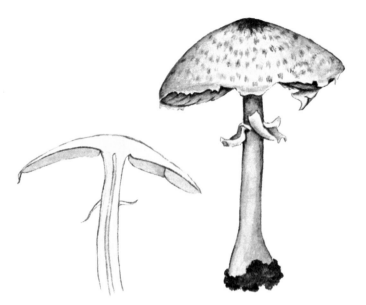

were capturing prison-
ers in battle, that they
were rich, that they pos-
sessed many slaves, that
they had committed adul-
tery and were to have their heads
crushed for the offense, that they
were guilty of a theft for which they
were to be killed, and many other visions which they saw. When the intoxication from the little mushrooms
had passed, they talked over among
themselves the visions they had seen."

Although there have been a few possible cases of poisoning from eating
these hallucinogenic mushrooms,
most users experience similar
results–hallucina-
tions (whether good
or bad), uncontrollable

19

movement, laughter, muscle weakness, and drowsiness.

Probably one of the best known of all mushrooms is Amanita muscaria. It is called the "Fly Agaric" because of the mushroom's reported ability to kill flies when pieces of it are mixed with milk. This mushroom has been the subject of much ethnobotanical literature. R.G. Wasson has speculated that this mushroom is the magic "Soma" of the ancient Aryan people. The Vedic priests suggested using it to experience ecstasy and to visualize eternal life.

The practice of shamanism by certain Siberian tribes involved the use of Amanita muscaria. The shaman or conjurer would induce his ceremonial trance by consuming dried pieces of this mushroom. Symptoms of the intoxication began with involuntary muscle jerking, dizziness, and drowsiness. Vomiting might follow. Later, sensations became intensified. Normal activities such as dancing, singing, and excessive talking were greatly exaggerated. These people regarded this mushroom so highly that their words

for trance, daze, and drunkenness are derived from the noun meaning "fungus, fly agaric."

The variety of toxins produced in mushrooms has long excited curiosity. Pliny thought that the explanation was obvious: "Noxious kinds must be entirely condemned; for if there be near them a hob-nail, or a bit of rusty iron, or a piece of rotten cloth, forthwith the plant, as it grows, elaborates the foreign juice and flavor into poison; who could discern the different kinds, except country-folk and

those who gather them? Moreover, they imbibe other noxious qualities besides; if, for instance, the hole of a venomous serpent be near, and the serpent breathes upon them, as they open, from their natural affinity with poisonous substances, they are readily disposed to imbibe such poison. Therefore, it will be well to exercise care in gathering them until the serpents retire into their holes." This belief persisted and found its way into some of the sixteenth century herbals.

But, as is the case of other unusual phenomena found in mushrooms, the explanation is one of biology and not the supernatural. Toxins are simply products of the metabolic activities of the mushroom.

For those who wish to become connoisseurs of mushrooms, the inevitable question is, "How do you separate the edible from the poisonous?"

From ancient times to the present day there have been many methods proposed for accomplishing this. Horace very generally states, "Fungi which grow in the meadows are best, it is not well to trust others." This statement is not true since there are some in fields that are poisonous and some that grow in forests that are good to eat.

Dioscorides discerned that poisonous mushrooms "have a thick coating of mucus, and when laid by after being gathered, quickly become putrid, but others not of this kind impart a sweet taste to sauces."

Certain empirical tests have been promoted from time to time to identify poisonous varieties. These tests purport to show that poisonous fungi have

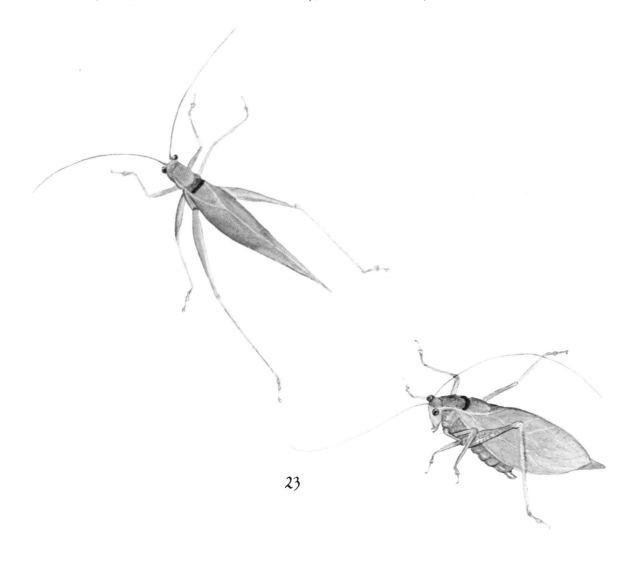

either a rep   ugnant appearance, are viscid, do not peel, have a fetid odor, exude a milky fluid, turn a different color rapidly upon breaking, yellow when sprinkled with salt, are acrid, hot, or bitter. Or that mushrooms nibbled on by insects, squirrels, or rabbits are safe to eat. Or that mushrooms which blacken a silver coin or silver spoon upon cooking or which turn an onion brown or blue are poison= ous. Fungi which grow on highly manured ground have been suspect.

Unfortunately, none of the above methods is val= id. The only sure way is to identify the various spe= cies. This knowledge can be acquired by studying the works of professional mycologists who have analyzed certain varieties for the presence of toxins.

Regardless of how hard one tries to separate ed= ible from poisonous mushrooms, poisonings will occur. The problem then arises as to the proper treatment. Classical remedies are abundant. The physician and poet Nicander proposed an elabo = rate concoction: "But do thou take the many~coated heads of the cabbage, or cut round the twisting stems of the rue, or take the efflorescence which has accumulated on old corroded copper, or steep the ashes of clematis in vinegar, then bruise the roots of pyrethrum, adding a sprinkling of lye or soda, and the leaf of cress which grows in the gardens, with the medic plant and pungent mustard, and burn wine-lees or the dung of the domestic fowl into ashes; then, putting your right finger in your throat to make you sick, vomit forth the baneful pest."

Almost all of the folk remedies functioned as emetics. Pliny proposed several substances to remove the fungus: mustard in vinegar, lily roots in wine, wormwood in vinegar, and others. Dioscorides was so cautious as to recommend an emetic even when eating mushrooms known to be safe: "As a safeguard, all should be eaten with a draught of olive oil and soda or lye ashes..., for even the edible sorts are difficult of digestion and generally pass whole with the excrement."

Even today most treatments begin with the administering of an emetic or other technique to remove the fungal material from the stomach. This may be followed by materials that absorb toxins and then by specific treatments for the type of poisoning.

Those interested in mushrooms, however, usually do not collect them because they are poisonous, but because they are edible. No one knows when man first discovered that fungi were edible. But there is considerable classical literature which indicates the passion that the Greeks and Romans possessed for eating certain fungi. However, they only considered a few mushrooms good to eat~boleti, suilli, and the truffle.

During the classical periods of history, the following recipe by Apicius was used to prepare one of the most sought-after delicacies, truffles.

"Boil, and sprinkle salt, transfix with a twig, partly roast, place in a cooking vessel with liquor, oil, greens, sweet boiled wine, a small quantity of unmixed wine, pepper and a little honey, and let it boil; while boiling beat up with fine flour; prick the tubers that they

26

may absorb, take out the twigs, and serve."

Martial, in an epigram, states, "We who, with tender head, burst through the earth that nourishes us, are truffles, a fruit second only to boleti."

The value placed upon the eating of certain fungi can be illustrated by the fact that this was the only food that the noblemen prepared themselves. The boleti (Amanita caesarea), the most highly prized of fungal delicacies, were cooked in special vessels called boletaria. These were not to be used for any inferior purpose. Martial expressed the lamentation of a boletaria whose function in a Roman kitchen had been changed, "Although boleti have given me such a noble name, I am now used, I am ashamed to say, for Brussels sprouts." The extensive use of mushrooms by the Romans was stimulated by the passage of sumptuary laws. These were passed to prevent ex-

travagant consumption of certain foods, in particular, meats. As a result many other types of foods
increased in popularity, among these certain fungi.

Cicero states," While these elegant eaters wish to
bring into high repute the products of the soil
which are not included in the Act, they prepare
their fungi, helvellae, and all vegetables with such
highly seasoned condiments that it is impossible
to conceive anything more delicious."

In another epigram Martial states," Gold and silver and dresses may be trusted to a messenger, but
not boleti." Obviously, it appears the temptation to
cook and eat them would be too great.

Not everyone, however, considered this highly
sought mushroom to be of reputable quality.
Galen, a famed physician, stated," Of fungi, the boletus, when well boiled, must be counted among the
insipid things." The reputation of this mushroom
was no doubt also tarnished due to the infamous

case of the death of the emperor Tiberius Claudius. According to Pliny, Claudius succumbed to a dish of boleti into which his wife, Agrippina, had placed or had ordered placed some poison, "by which she inflicted another poison upon the world, and especially on herself, in the person of her son, Nero."

The passion of some people in the United States for eating mushrooms has undoubtedly been influenced by their European ancestry. This inherited desire is fortified by the wide variety found to grow in this country. Charles McIlvaine, one of the pioneers of mushroom eating in the United States, ate and recommended over 700 varieties while roaming the forests of West Virginia in the late 1800s.

There is documentation that the American Indians used mushrooms for food. But there is little evidence to show that they were considered delica-

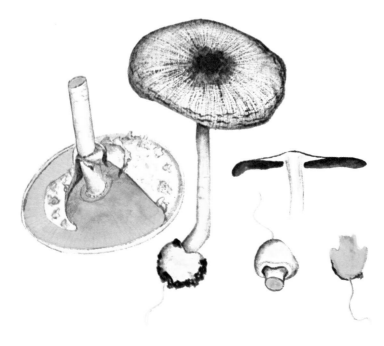

cies. Some Indians apparently ate all mushrooms. The Tewa Indians of the Southwest did not appear to distinguish between edible or poisonous varieties and apparently suffered no ill effects.

Certain varieties were apparently preferred by various Indian tribes. The Dakota ate Polystictus versicolor; the Omaha and Pawnee ate the corn smut fungus, Ustilago maydis; the Omaha also ate the common morel, Morchella esculenta. The Thompson Indians of British Columbia prepared species of Agaricus by hanging them up to dry. They were then cut into pieces, peeled, and eaten raw. Sometimes they were roasted for a few minutes.

The Alaskan Eskimo have some interesting uses for fungi. One does not directly involve eating. The Eskimo use tobacco for smoking, chewing, and dipping snuff. One technique involves the mixing of finely ground tobacco with the ash of a certain tree fungus. This mixture is then kneaded and rolled into

30

rounded pellets. The men do not usually chew the pellets, but they hold them in the cheek and rarely expectorate the juice. Thus, the imaginative mycophagist can use mushrooms many different ways.

Reportedly, certain poisonous mushrooms can be rendered edible with very simple treatment. In 1850, Frédéric Gérard published an account of his experiments in which poisonous varieties, Amanita muscaria and Amanita phalloides, were cut into large pieces, washed, and soaked for two hours in water to which vinegar was added. The pieces were then removed, washed again, and boiled in wa-

ter for ½ hour. Finally, they were washed again after which the pieces were prepared in the normal way for the table. Gérard reported that he and his family ate over 200 pounds of poisonous mushrooms within one month. Although a special commission of the Conseil de Salubrité of Paris accepted his technique as effective, it is not recommended that poisonous mushrooms be eaten under any circumstances.

Henri Fabre, a renowned French naturalist, stated that he and his family, as well as others in southern France, regularly ate poisonous mushrooms, such as Amanita pantherina and Boletus satan-

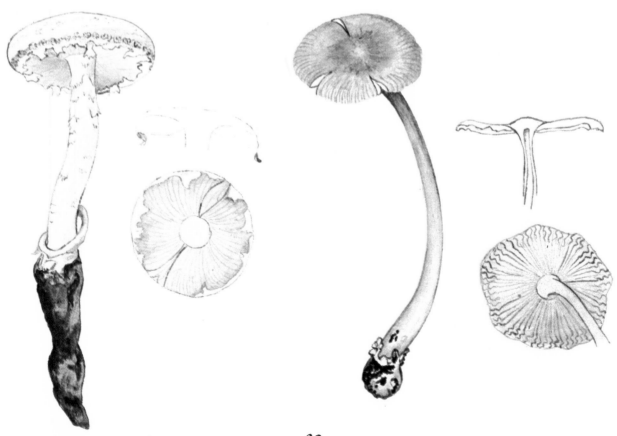

us. These were simply prepared by boiling them in salty water and then rinsing them in water. Fabre revealed, "During the thirty and more years that I have lived in Sérignan, I have never heard of one case of mushroom poisoning, even the mildest, in the village." In certain European markets wild mushrooms can be bought just as readily as fruits and vegetables. Though experts have identified as many as 300 varieties in European markets, you may not find as many as 5 at a time at any given market.

The Greeks and Romans theorized that certain mushrooms could be induced to grow under special conditions. Dioscorides relates, "Some people say that the bark of the white and black poplar cut into small pieces and scattered over dunged species will produce edible fungi at all seasons." In the Geoponica, an anonymous work of about A.D. 900, a recipe is given for mushroom cultivation: "In order to make fungi grow, one must saw off the stump of a black poplar and pour sour dough dissolved in water upon the cut pieces. Black poplar fungi soon appear."

Through the years different countries have developed different preferences concerning commercial mushroom production. In the United States the only mushroom produced in abundance is Agaricus bisporus, a close relative of the common field mushroom Agaricus campestris. This mushroom can be bought in many supermarkets and can be ordered in many restaurants.

Other countries, however, have their own specialities, such as Lentinus edodes, the shii-take in Japan, and Auricularia auricula in China. The paddy straw mushroom, Volvariella volvacea, is also popular in southeast Asia. The world's production of cultivated mushrooms is estimated at over 1,700,000,000 pounds per year.

France is known for its sale of the truffle. Although its growth is not controlled by commercial tech-

34

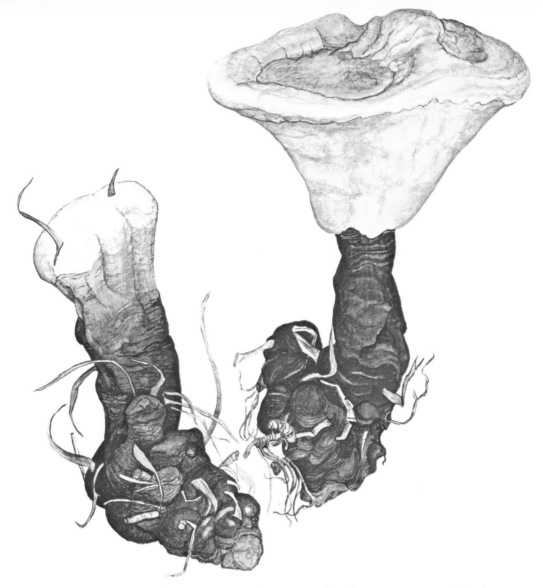

niques as the others mentioned, the truffle is collected
in abundance and exported to other countries. Truffles
have been known to sell for up to $300 per dry pound.
One of the most interesting facts concerning truffle
cultivation is the method of collecting. These organisms grow underground making them very difficult
to find. Some truffles produce strong odors. These are
reliably detected by animals such as wildcats, wolves,
bears, deer, goats, rabbits, squirrels, and others. There
is one animal, however, whose talent has long since
been utilized to aid in truffle collection--the pig. In

the Périgord region of southwestern France, reported to produce the world's best black truffle, the female pig has long been used to sniff out these subterranean delicacies. Their natural instinct has also been traditionally utilized in other European countries.

The rooting ability of this animal was a natural for unearthing the truffle. The Diary of Evelyn (1644) recounts,"Here we supped and lay, having amongst other dainties, a dish of truffles, which is a certain earthnut, found by a hogg trained to it, and for which those animals are sold at a great price."

The truffier may put a muzzle on the pig or keep in reserve a potato to distract the pig so that it will not eat the prize.

Dogs, although not natural hunters of truffles, are frequently trained to hunt these delicacies. This technique appears to have originated in Italy. There is a school near Genoa which is famed for its production of truffle hounds. This school has been in existence for over 200 years. In certain European countries the possession of one of these specially trained dogs is considered a status symbol. These dogs have been known to detect the scent of a truffle at over 100 yards.

If you are not fortunate enough to own a talented hog or dog, other techniques are used to find truffles. Types of flies, called truffle flies, like to lay their eggs in mature truffles. As the truffles ripen, swarms of flies can be seen hovering about the truffle location. One only has to spot the swarm and dig.

Whether you are an avid mycophagist in search of the many edible wild mushrooms or are content with those commercially grown, you are in for an unparalleled treat when they are prepared for the table. Let your imagination guide you. Endless ways can be found to enjoy these woodland delicacies. For those of you who appreciate the miracles of nature and would translate some of these wonders from their woodland home to your table, you will be rewarded with some of the most exquisite tastes imaginable.

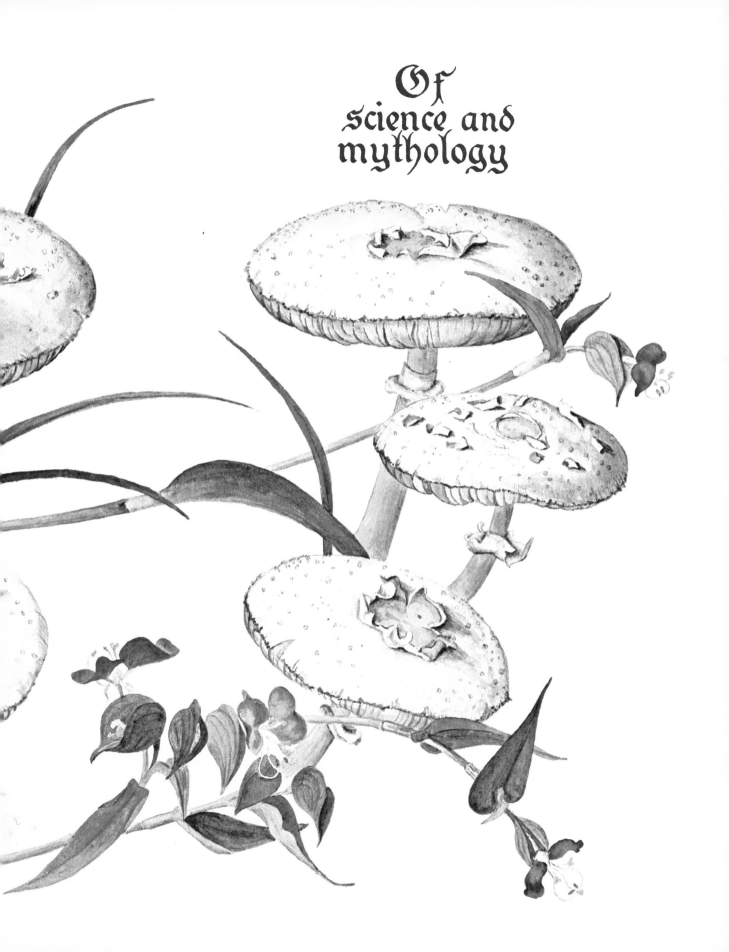

Of science and mythology

By now you have become increasingly aware of the uniqueness of the group of organisms called mushrooms. This uniqueness has triggered curiosity and fantasy throughout history. Not surprisingly, the contradictions and strange phenomena associated with mushrooms have inspired myths.

A most interesting phenomenon resulting from the growth of mushrooms is the production of the "fairy ring." As the name implies, considerable folklore is associated with this structure.

> The nimble elves,
> That do by moonshine green sour ringlets make,
> Whereof the ewe bites not; whose pastime tis,
> To make these midnight mushrooms.
>
> Rev. Gerard Smith

Much of the myth associated with fairy rings is probably related to the unusual patterns produced in the grass. Frequently, there will be a ring of dark green grass, apparently growing more luxuriantly than the surrounding grass. This encloses another very conspicuous ring of dead grass. Finally, inside, there is another zone in which the growth of the grass is apparently stimulated. In total, the pattern produced is one of concentric rings.

Fairy rings, also called fairy rounds, fairy dances, and fairy walks, are usually related to

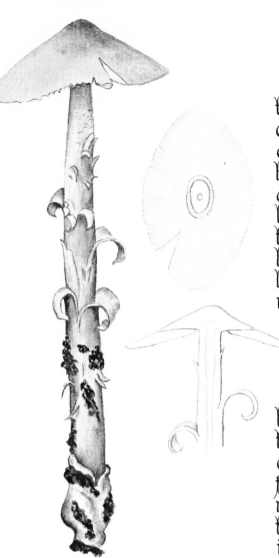

the "wee people" engaged in some circular activity. One legend envisions the elves joining hands and dancing in a circle all night under the moon= light. If the night is dark, they use a glowworm for a light. The mushrooms, which later grow around the outer margin of the ring, provide seats upon which the elves can sit and play their musical instruments.

Depending upon where you lived, superstition might dic= tate evil or good results after one came in contact with fairy rings. In England, if a maiden washed her face with the dew of the grass from inside a ring, the fairies would take revenge upon her by spoiling her complexion.

It was thought to be good fortune to have fairy rings growing in fields adjacent to your own. On the other hand, if the rings were found growing in your fields, it was quite unfortu= nate. It was especially unfortunate if you stepped inside one.

There was also the possibility that a special treasure was buried within these rings but was guarded by witches and fairies.

> He wha tills the fairies green,
> Nae luck again shall hae;
> And he wha spills the fairies ring,
> Betide him want and wae;
> For wierdless days and weary night,
> Are his to his deein day.

Traditional

Not only was it dangerous for people to be associated with these rings, but animals also could be affected. One Danish superstition goes:"It is necessary to watch cattle, that they may not graze in any place where the Elle-people have been; for if any animal come to a place where the Elle-people have spit, or done what is worse, it is attacked by some grievous disease, which can only be cured by giving it to eat a handful of St.John's Wort, which had been pulled at twelve o'clock on St.John's night."

The pliability of superstition allows for explanations of ring production other than those associated with fairies. In Germany, these rings were said to be produced by a gathering of

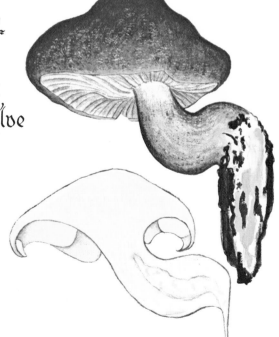

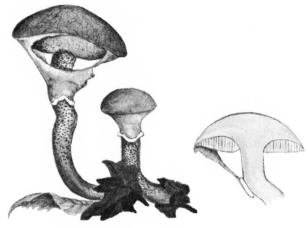

witches who celebrate Walpurgis night by dancing. Dragons were also indicted as being responsible, either by scorching the fields with fiery tails or by resting after nightly adventures. The Dutch believed that these rings were the resting places of the devil's churns. In France, it was thought that enormous toads frequently occupied the rings. Anyone intentionally entering a ring could expect trouble.

Eventually, people began to supply more "scientific" explanations for the formation of these rings. In 1718, Bradley gave an explanation for the fairy ring formation that involved the activity of snails: "...when they couple, always make choice of short grass to creep upon. It is their manner, when they generate, to take a large compass upon the ground, and meet one another. Thus I have seen them creep into a circle for more than half an hour, going over the same ground at least twenty times before they could join, leaving upon the grass where they crept, a viscous, shiny matter. So that it may be, that slime, when it

44

putrifies, may produce the mushrooms we find growing in circles upon commons; and I am more apt to believe it so, because I have more than once observed, that where a snail has left a track upon the grass, a few days afterwards I have found mushrooms to come up. But it must be observed, that such as come up in this manner are not fit to eat."

Other "scientific" explanations were just as fanciful. Anything that might have moved in a circle was suspect: ants, moles, horses, birds, and deer. Some even thought that whirlwinds could be the cause.

The explanation which probably gained more acceptance than any other involved the explosion of lightning. You recall the suspected involvement of thunder and lightning in the production of truffles. It was just as easy to accept

45

the theory that fairy rings were produced by these spectacular, natural phenomena. As early as 1563, W. Fulke postulated that these rings were the result of the effects of lightning. In 1686, Robert Plot offered a more detailed explanation as to the involvement of lightning in fairy ring production. He finally concluded that "they must needs be the effects of lightning, exploded from the clouds, most times in a circular manner." His theoretical explanation concluded, "The explosion of lightning when it first breaks the clouds presses equally outward on every side, so 'tis like it may retain the same tendency after it has striken the earth in such rings as are entire." In 1790, Erasmus Darwin wrote in Botanic Garden:
So from dark clouds the playful lightning springs,
Rives the firm Oak, or prints the fairy rings.

It was not until the end of the eighteenth century that the growth of mushrooms was credited with fairy ring production. William Withering concluded in 1792, "I am satisfied that the bare and brown, or highly clothed and verdant circles, in pasture fields, called Fairy Rings, are caused by the growth of this Agaric." He was referring to the mushroom now called Marasmius oreades.

Another explanation of the fairy ring followed in the nineteenth century. The mushroom is only a reproductive structure. Most of the mycelium that composes a fungus is underground and originated from the germination of a single spore.

When a spore lands in soil that contains suffi-
cient nutrients and moisture, germination occurs.
Since these nutrients are usually distributed
throughout the soil, the hyphae will tend to
grow in all directions. And because oxygen is
required for growth, they will grow nearer
the surface.

As long as nutrients remain available, the
mycelium will continue to grow outward
from the point of origin. Imagine this by com-

paring it to a match thrown into a field of dry grass and continuing to spread outward as long as there is grass to burn. This theory does not, of course, account for the three concentric rings.

In 1917, Schantz and Piemeisel provided a possible explanation for this phenomenon. As the ring of mycelium continues to expand, the resulting chemical action at the outermost edge apparently alters the nutrient materials in the soil. This stimulates the growth of the grass in that zone. In this ring, mushrooms will be produced at certain times of the year and under the appropriate environmental and nutritional conditions. Within this ring is found the greater part of the subterranean mycelium. Apparently, through the physical action of the mycelium and the consumption of nutrients by the fungus, the growth of the grass is inhibited. Thereby, the second ring of dead grass is produced.

As the mycelium on the outer margin continues to grow, the hyphae toward the inside die and decompose, releasing a concentration of nutrients back into the soil. As a re-

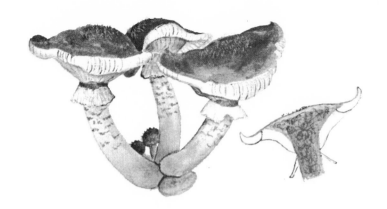

sult, the grass in that zone will again flourish.
Thus, the inner ring of stimulated growth is
produced. When the growth of these rings from
year to year has been observed, increases in
size of several inches to several feet per year
have been noted. By measuring the diameter,
some rings have been estimated at over 500
years in age.

Much of the folklore associated with the
mushroom originated as a result of some
strange, biological phenomenon, such as the
bioluminescence, color changes of the flesh, rapid growth, odd shapes, and poisonous qualities.

In discussing the strange phenomena associated with the growth of a mushroom, we naturally relate growth to an increase in size.
There have been instances in which a section
of a concrete sidewalk, weighing in excess of
100 pounds, has been raised several inches by
the growth of specimens of the green spored
Chlorophyllum molybdites. Also, there have
been reports of several mushrooms growing
up through an asphalt driveway which was

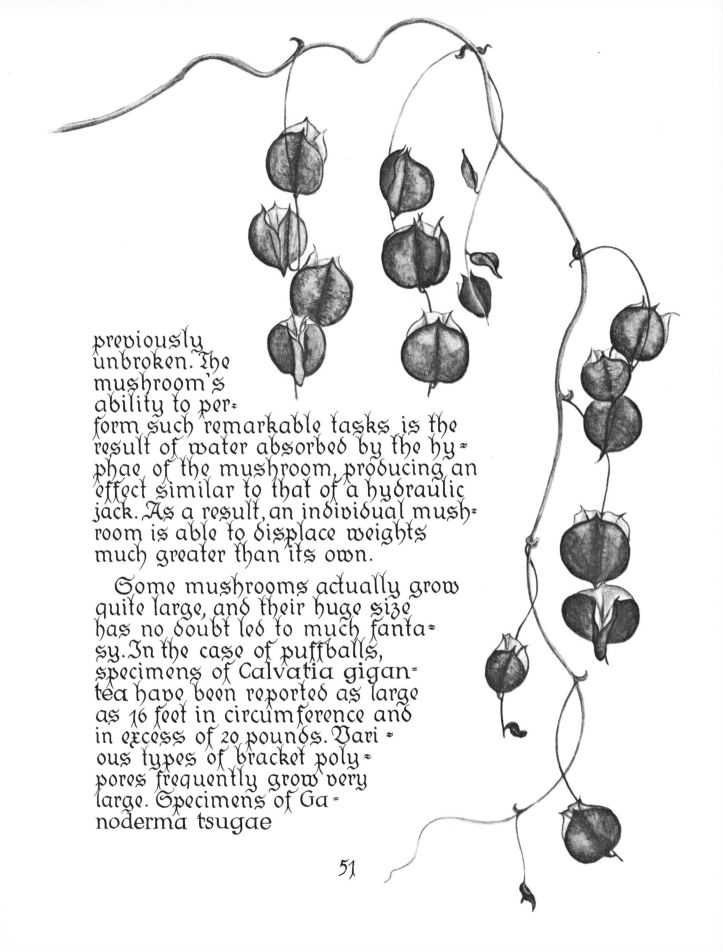

previously
unbroken. The
mushroom's
ability to per=
form such remarkable tasks is the
result of water absorbed by the hy=
phae of the mushroom, producing an
effect similar to that of a hydraulic
jack. As a result, an individual mush=
room is able to displace weights
much greater than its own.

Some mushrooms actually grow
quite large, and their huge size
has no doubt led to much fanta=
sy. In the case of puffballs,
specimens of Calvatia gigan=
tea have been reported as large
as 16 feet in circumference and
in excess of 20 pounds. Vari=
ous types of bracket poly=
pores frequently grow very
large. Specimens of Ga=
noderma tsugae

51

have been known to reach five feet in diameter. It is not uncommon to collect mushrooms that are 5 to 6 inches in diameter. Specimens of Catathelasma imperialis, however, have been reported at 2 feet in diameter. Since mushrooms are composed mostly of water, these larger specimens are usually found in the damper, forested areas of the United States.

We must also realize, however, that the growth we see is the result of certain biochemical reactions that we do not see. Many of the biochemical reactions that

52

are part of a mushroom's metabolism result in the production of interesting phenomena other than those expressed by physical growth. Many of these occurrences are associated with the production of metabolic by-products that apparently make little contribution to the survival of the mushroom.

One category of by-products that has already been discussed is toxins. An interesting toxin that has not been mentioned, however, is produced by Gyromitra esculenta. As implied by the species name, this mushroom is edible and is fre=

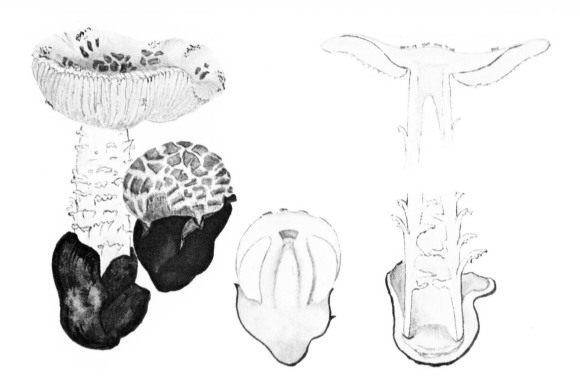

quently sought for the table. Poisoning cases
are rare. But it does produce a toxin called mo=
nomethylhydrazine. Interestingly, this substance
has been used by the United States Air Force
as a rocket fuel.

Of the many varieties of mushrooms that one
might collect, quite a few possess an interest=
ing characteristic. When the flesh of the mush=
room is cut or bruised, a rapid color change takes
place. Some of the most spectacular of these
changes are found within the genus Boletus.
In several species, such as Boletus fraternus
and Boletus miniato-olivaceus, the flesh, upon
being cut, rapidly turns a bright blue to blue
green. You can imagine the stories that might
result from someone who, for the first time, has
collected one of these mushrooms and begins to
prepare it for eating.

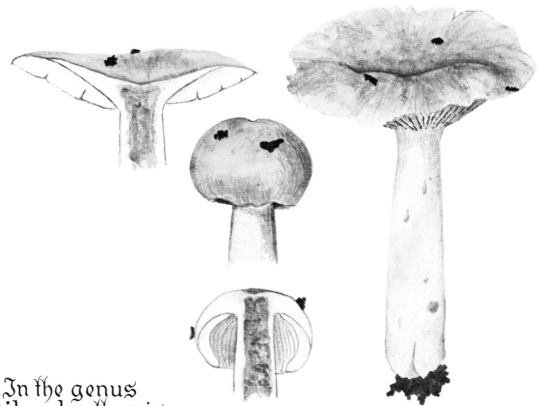

In the genus
Psilocybe, there is
a color change
which is associated with those species that contain hallucinogenic toxins. Handling these specimens will cause a distinct bluing of the mushrooms' flesh, which is due to some toxin conversions within the mushrooms. This reaction is also found in a few other genera which possess these same toxins.

Several members of the genus Amanita also exhibit color changes when the mushroom's flesh is bruised: reddish in Amanita rubescens, brownish in Amanita brunnescens, and a golden yellow in Amanita crassifolia. There are species of the bracket fungus, Ganoderma, whose pore surface turns brownish when damaged. The large fruit bodies common to this genus have been

55

used as a "painting canvas" on which beautiful nature scenes have been drawn, using only the cream-colored background of the pore surface and the resulting brown stains.

Mushrooms have as many different odors as they have tastes. Though many mushrooms have a fairly neutral smell (one that is usually referred to as "fungoid"), there are numerous smells which are quite distinct. Certain Amanitas produce a smell commonly called "chloride of lime." An odor which might remind you of fresh ground meal is called "farinaceous." Some odors are very similar to those of fresh fruit. But there are unpleasant as well as pleasant odors. The greenish or brownish spore mass, found on mushrooms called stink horns, emits a very disagreeable odor.

The names applied to many odors are the result of the collector trying to relate them to something familiar. One of the pioneer mycologists in the United States had an interesting talent for naming

56

odors. In naming odors of certain Amanitas, W. C. Coker used such descriptive phrases as "fresh cut grass," "green peanuts," "radishes," "smoked ham," and "old ham."

A characteristic used to separate members of the genus Lacta= rius is the production of various-colored la= tex, which is apparent= ly a metabolic by-pro= duct. Upon cutting the gills or flesh, this milky latex will e= merge. The color varies with the species: white, cream, yellow, green, orange, blue, purple, and various gradations. Fre= quently, the latex will emerge as one color and dry to another color. The taste of the milk is al= so distinctive--sweet, astringent, bitter, hot, farinaceous, and others.

There is one final pro= duct of metabolism a=

58

bout which there has probably been more fanciful speculation than any other. This is the phenomenon of luminosity. Bioluminescence, the natural production of light by living organisms, is a well-known phenomenon found in numerous groups of insects and fishes. And it is not an uncommon occurrence in the "separate kingdom." Quite a few mushrooms are known to "glow in the dark." Some of the more common luminescent mushrooms in the United States are Armillariella mellea, Clitocybe illudens, and Panellus stypticus. Those of you who enjoy backpacking may

have happened upon a strange light some dark night while hiking. At first you may have thought that you were seeing fireflies or someone's lantern. You may have finally discovered that this eerie glow was produced by a luminous mushroom. Or, you may not have wanted to discover the source at all!

Several young people were walking through the forest on a very dark night. Upon rounding a bend in the narrow, dirt road, they were suddenly confronted with a long, luminous band in the center of the road. The streak glowed with an unnatural phosphorescence, and their first response was to run. But their natural curiosity overcame them. Upon examining the glowing line, they found hundreds of bits of wood permeated with luminous hyphae. An investigation revealed that a logging crew had been dragging logs along this road during the day. One of the logs had been infected with a bioluminescent fungus. As it was dragged along, it left a mysterious trail that could only be seen during the night.

Depending upon the particular species of mushroom, various parts of the fruit body may glow. In Armillariella mellea, commonly called the "Honey Mushroom" or the "Shoe-string Root Rot Fungus," the mycelium within the log on which it is growing is luminous. In Clitocybe illudens, (the "Jack-O'-Lantern Mushroom") and Panellus stypticus, the gills glow. In some tropical species

60

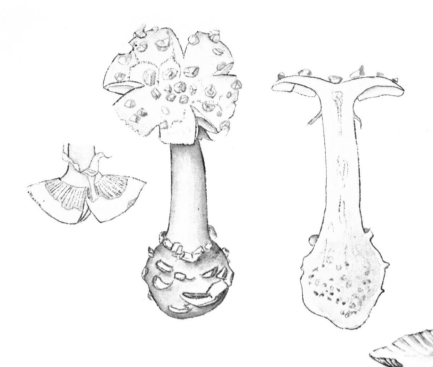

the entire fruit body glows,
while in some, such as My=
cena rorida, only the spores
that fall on the ground pro=
duce light. The color of the
light will vary, depending up=
on the variety of mushroom,
from white to bluish white,
bluish green, greenish white,
or greenish. The light produced
may last for hours or days.

The luminescent property of
certain mushrooms was not
unknown to the ancients, al=
though it did not play a signif=
icant role in their folklore. In
speaking of the Agaricum, Fo=
mes officinalis, Pliny states,

"The acorn~producing trees in the Gallic provinces more particularly produce agaricum; it is a white fungus with strong odor, useful as an antidote; it grows on the tops of trees and shines at night, by which fact its presence is known and it is gathered."

The tropical regions of the world display a greater number of luminescent mushrooms than the more temperate regions. An enchanting description is given by the naturalist H. O. Forbes of a scene in a forest in Sumatra: "The stem of every tree blinked with a pale greenish white light which undulated also across the surface of the ground like moonlight coming and going behind the clouds, from a minute thread~like fungus invisible in the daytime to the unassisted eye; and

here and there thick, dumpy mushrooms displayed a sharp, clear dome of light, whose intensity never varied or changed till the break of day; long phosphorescent caterpillars and centipedes crawled out of every corner, leaving a trail of light behind them, while fireflies darted about above like a lower firmament."

Many of the natives that live in these tropical habitats take advantage of this unique property. Some are used as nighttime decorations. The mushrooms may be picked and laid beside a particularly dangerous path to show the way. Maidens may be seen wearing them in their hair. Young boys may simply play with them as a curiosity, sometimes sticking the mushrooms all over their bodies.

Ramsbottom relates that an American war correspondant in New Guinea wrote to his wife, "Darling, I am writing to you tonight by the

light of five mushrooms."
During the World Wars,
troops were known to
stick luminescent mush=
rooms on their helmets
and rifles to avoid colli=
sions on dark nights. In a
London timber yard, some
of the wood glowed so bright=
ly on dark nights that tarpau=
lins were used to cover it so that enemy aircraft
could not see it. Because this light does not emit
heat, it has been used in buildings where com =
bustible materials (such as hay and grains)
have to be stored.

Could this eerie manifestation have any prac=
tical value for the mushroom or any other organ=
ism? The possibility exists that certain night ~
flying insects are attracted to the glowing
mushrooms. These insects, in turn, may lay their

eggs in the mushroom
or pick up some fungus
spores for dissemination.

We have observed nu=
merous phenomena result=
ing from mushrooms as in=
dividual organisms. It is not
unusual to find unique associa=
tions between mushrooms and other
living organisms. One of the most inter =
esting of these associations involves the cultiva=
tion of fungi by certain types of ants and termites.
In many tropical and subtropical areas of the
world, certain genera of ants and termites have de=
veloped an astounding talent for cultivating certain
types of fungi in their nests. The ants which en=
gage in this curious task are known as leaf cut=
ters. Observers have seen them strip the foliage
from a large tree overnight. There had long been
speculation as to the use of these leaves. Some

67

thought they were used as food; others surmised that the leaves were used to line their nests. It is now known that leaves are brought into the nests by specific ants. Others take the leaves and cut them into tiny pieces. These are finally used as

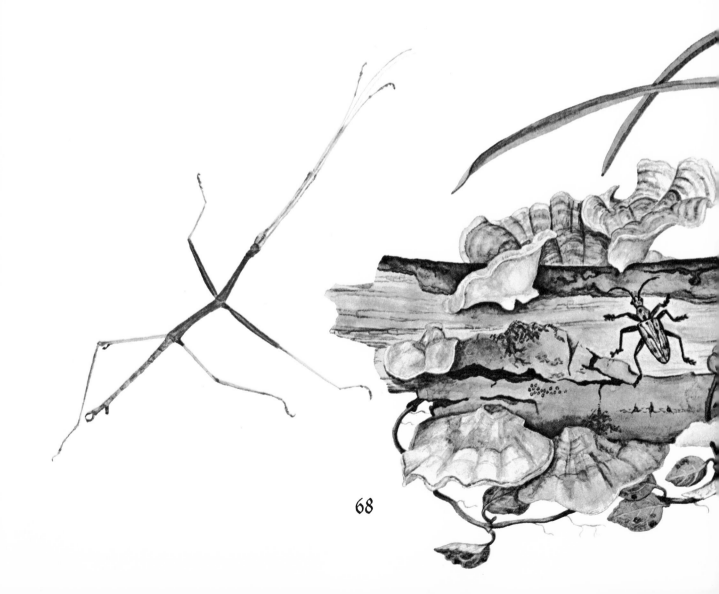

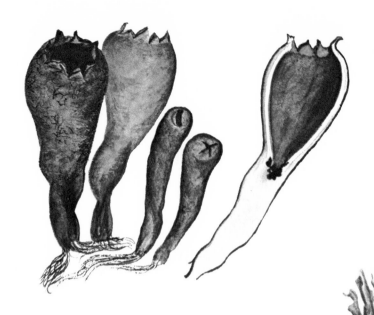

a culture medium for growing
a specific fungus, which is used
as food, especially for the young.
Other ants (nurses) move among
the young, feeding them the fungus
as needed. Amazingly enough, this
fungus is grown in the nests with
very little contamination from other fungi. The ants are evidently able to accomplish
this by controlling the humidity and temperature
in the chambers to suit the particular fungus. It
is also possible that certain ants remove contam-
inants as they move through the crops. This talent
is quite remarkable considering that professional
mycologists must use very exacting conditions
and specialized equipment to produce and main-
tain contaminant~free cultures in the laboratory.

The nests of these ants are quite large.
They consist of many chambers, up to

70

several feet in diameter, and are connected by tun=
nels. Complexes of these chambers have been re=
corded to cover an area of 250 to 300 feet. The low
mounds of dirt, produced by the digging of these
chambers, have been measured at up to 120 feet
in circumference. Several different types of mushrooms have been identified as the ant~fungus,
especially certain species of the genus Lepiota.

Some types of termites are also known to cul=
tivate species of fungi. This cultivation may take

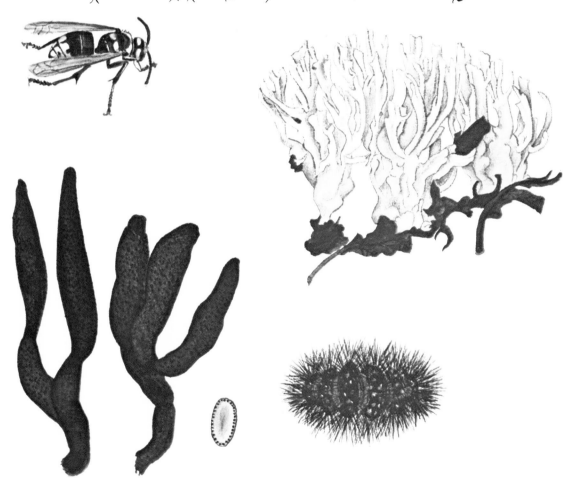

place in underground chambers, similar to those of the ants, or in chambers above the ground found in large mounds up to 6 feet in height and 16 feet in diameter. Such mushrooms as Lentinus, Collybia, Pluteus, Armillaria, and Volvariella have been associated with termite nests.

One of the most ecologically important associations involves mushrooms and higher plants. This relationship is called mycorrhizae. It develops between the very small roots of the plant and the hyphae of the fungus. It was originally supposed that this was a parasitic relationship — that the fungus benefited to the detriment of the tree. Today, we realize that under normal conditions both partners benefit.

In many mycorrhizal associations the fungus grows around and into the plant roots. By doing

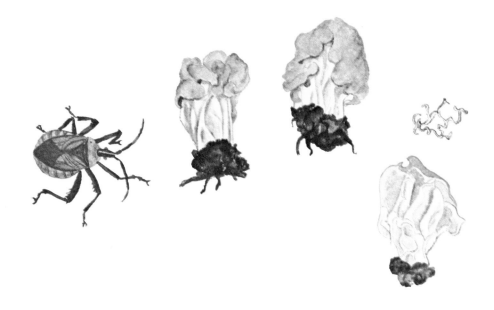

this, the surface area of the root, through which nutrient materials are absorbed, is increased. In addition, the fungus often can break down complex nutrient materials for absorption that the plant ordinarily could not accomplish alone. In return, the fungus receives certain nutrient materials resulting from the metabolic processes of the tree. At times a mycorrhizal relationship may be so necessary that neither partner can survive without the other.

Still another interesting association, that does not appear to have as great an ecological impact as does mycorrhizae, is between a fungus and an alga. This is called a lichen. You have probably seen greenish, grayish green, or brownish patches on trees or rocks. Lichens are very durable and are found in many terrestrial

habitats. They are particularly abundant in mountainous areas. It is thought that the fungus gains nutrients from the photosynthetic abilities of the alga. The advantage for the alga, however, is not clearly understood; it may simply be one of protection.

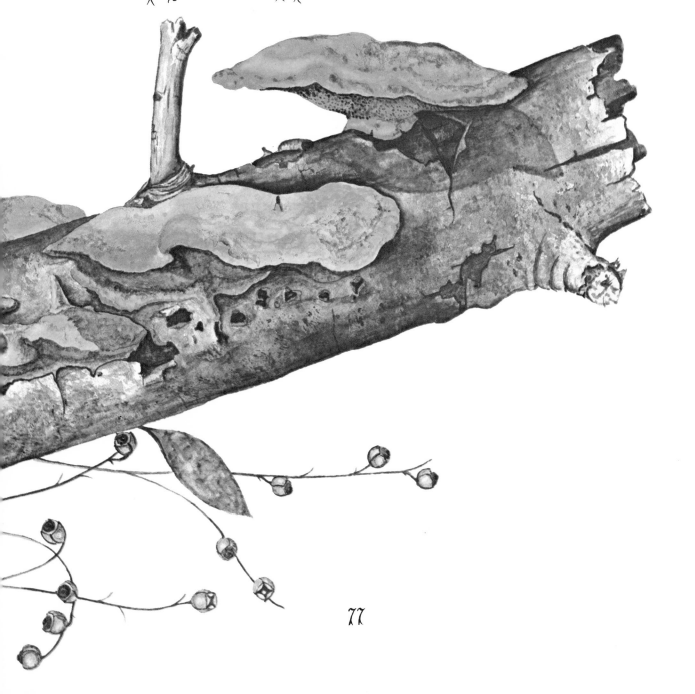

Lichens are very slow in growing, as little as 1 millimeter per year. This is due to the requirements of high humidity, cooler temperatures, and low light intensities. These conditions are usually found only for a few hours each morning. The age of some lichens has been estimated at approximately 4500 years.

The fungal associations which probably have the greatest immediate effect upon mankind are those producing diseases of food crops. Each year millions of dollars worth of crops are destroyed due to the pathogenic nature of certain fungi, particularly, those which cause diseases commonly called the rusts and smuts. These fungi usually attack certain kinds of grain, such as wheat, oats, and corn.

Probably the best known of these diseases is

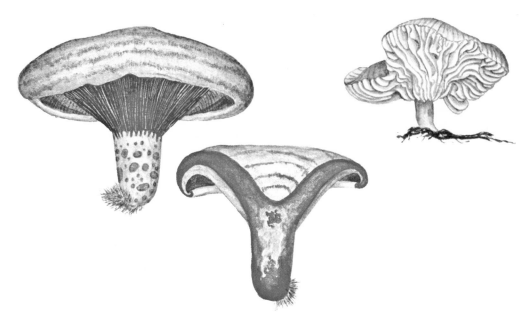

stem rust of wheat. This disease is quite conspicuous due to the bright orange to rusty brown masses of spores found on the plant. Wheat rust is still common today. Several epidemics have occurred in the United States and Canada with damage during a single growing season amounting to between 200 and 300 million dollars. Control of this disease is not easy, but resistant varieties of wheat are continually being developed. Usually, however, these are soon attacked by new varieties of rust fungi. Stem rust of wheat is a classical disease and has received considerable attention from Biblical times to the present day.

The ancient Greeks and Romans were well aware of this disease. It was mentioned by such scholars as Aristotle, Theophrastus, Ovid, and Pliny. Pliny referred to the rust as "the greatest

79

pest of the crops." He suggested that this disease was caused by the sun heating dew drops on the wheat. He further suggested that this disease could be controlled by "fixing branches of laurel in the fields, for then the rust passes over the laurel leaves."

As a precaution, the Romans had a festival each year on the 25th of April called the Robigalia. Its purpose was to stimulate the god Robigus, who was supposed to have the power to control this disease. A proces-

sion left Rome headed for the sacred grove. Before a crowd dressed in white togas, the priest offered up prayers to the rust god asking for his help. Wine was poured onto the altar, incense was burned, and the entrails of a sheep and a rust~colored dog were burned on the altar. With the advent of modern fungicides, however, the rust god, Robigus, has since been discarded.

Another disease that, historically, had considerable economic impact was late blight of potatoes. The fungus responsible for this disease was Phytophthora infestans. The most devastating example of this disease was in Ireland in 1845. The potato was the staple food crop of the Irish. As a result of the failure of the potato crop, approximately 1 mil=

lion people died and 1.5 million emigrated to other countries, the United States being the most frequently~chosen destination.

Many of the superstitions to which people have subscribed concerning fungi were harmless. Most were simply attempts to explain curious happenings, but some of the superstitions concerning medicinal properties of fungi were potentially deadly.

It was not uncommon for certain curative powers to be assigned to specific fungi which actually had none. Dioscorides, for example, believed that the Agaricum, Fomes officinalis, was an extremely powerful medicinal agent. "Its properties are styptic and heat~producing, efficacious against colic and sores, fractured limbs, and bruises from falls; the dose is two obols weight with wine and honey to those who have no fever; in fever cases with honeyed water; it is given in liver complaints, asthma, jaundice, dysentery, kidney diseases where

there is difficulty in passing water, in cases of hysteria, and to those of a sallow complexion, in doses of one drachma; in cases of phthisis it is administered in raisin wine, in affections of the spleen with honey and vinegar. By persons troubled with pains in the stomach and by those who suffered from acid eructations, the root is chewed and swallowed by itself without any liquid; it stops bleeding when taken with water in three obol doses; it is good for pain in the loins and joints, in epilepsy when taken with an equal quantity of honey and vinegar....It prevents rigor if taken before the attack; in one and two drachma doses, it acts as a purgative when taken with honeyed water; it is an antidote in poisons in one drachma doses with dilute wine. In three obol doses with wine it is a relief in cases of bites and wounds caused by serpents. On the whole it is serviceable in all internal complaints when taken according to the age and strength of the patient, some should take it with water, others with wine, and others with vinegar and honey or with water and honey." It is obvious that Dioscorides greatly exaggerated the medicinal power of this fungus.

This was not the only fungus thought to have extraordinary properties. "It was thought that the Boleti were good for the stomach. The Suilli...remove freckles and blemishes on women's faces; a healing lotion is also made of them, as of lead, for sore eyes; soaked in water they are applied as a salve to foul ulcers and eruptions of the head and

to bites inflicted by dogs." One of the oldest recorded medicinal uses of fungi was cauterization. Hippocrates' writings included this remedy. One such example among the Laplanders involved spreading bits of dried mushrooms on the body part where there was pain. This material was then set on fire. The burning caused blisters and the discharge of water supposedly carried away the pain.

Not all of the more unusual medicinal uses of fungi date back to the times of the Greeks and Romans, however. The powdery spores from the Earth

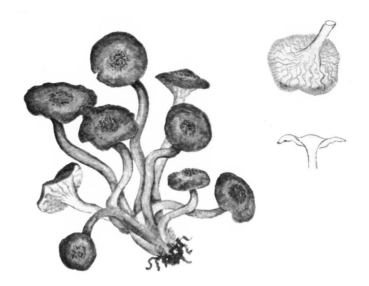

Star puffball were used by the Tewa Indians of California as a remedy for ear infections; the spores were blown into the ear through a tube of corn husk.

Various Indian tribes in the Missouri River region used the spores of several puffballs as a styptic for most wounds, as well as on the umbilicus of newborns.

An interesting contrast to this is the folklore in Scotland in which the spores from a puffball, called the devil's snuff box, are supposed to cause blindness.

One of the most unusual attempts to use certain fungi as medicinal agents was associated with astrology. In Culpepper's Complete Herbal, mushrooms were associated with certain astrological signs and were, therefore, presumably able to cure certain ailments. Some mushrooms, which were controlled by Mercury under Aries, had medicinal properties. When roasted and applied in a poultice or boiled with white lily roots in milk, they supposedly ripened boils and abscesses better than any preparation. According to this book their poultices were of service in quinces and inflammatory swellings.

Then there are the myths that do not apparently originate from factual occurrence. In Poland there is a myth which is directed toward explaining the production of edible and poisonous mushrooms. When Christ and Peter were passing through a forest after a long journey without food, Peter, who had a loaf in his sack but did not take it out for fear of offending his Master, slipped a piece in his mouth. Christ, who was in front, spoke to him at the moment and Peter

spat out so that he could answer. This occurred
several times until the loaf was finished. Wherever Peter spat out, edible fungi appeared. The
devil, who was walking behind, saw this and
decided to go one better by producing brighter
and more highly colored mushrooms. He spat
mouthfuls of bread all over the countryside. These
wonderfully colored mushrooms which looked
very much like St. Peter's mushrooms, were, however, all poisonous.

One of the most spectacular myths deals with
the production of one of the best known of all
mushrooms, the Fly Agaric, Amanita muscaria.
The dominant character in this myth was Woten, one of the Germanic gods. One day Woten

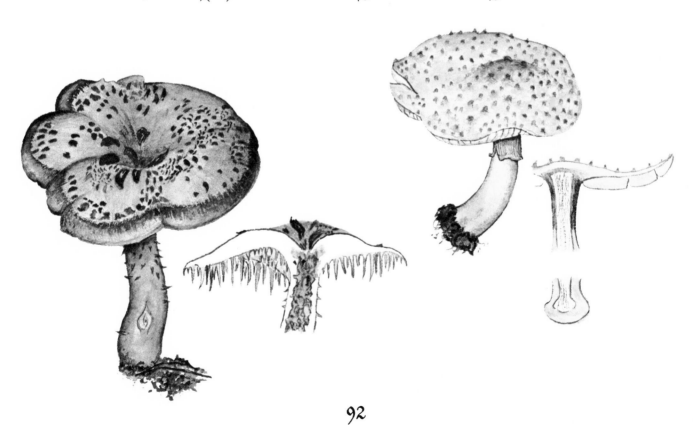

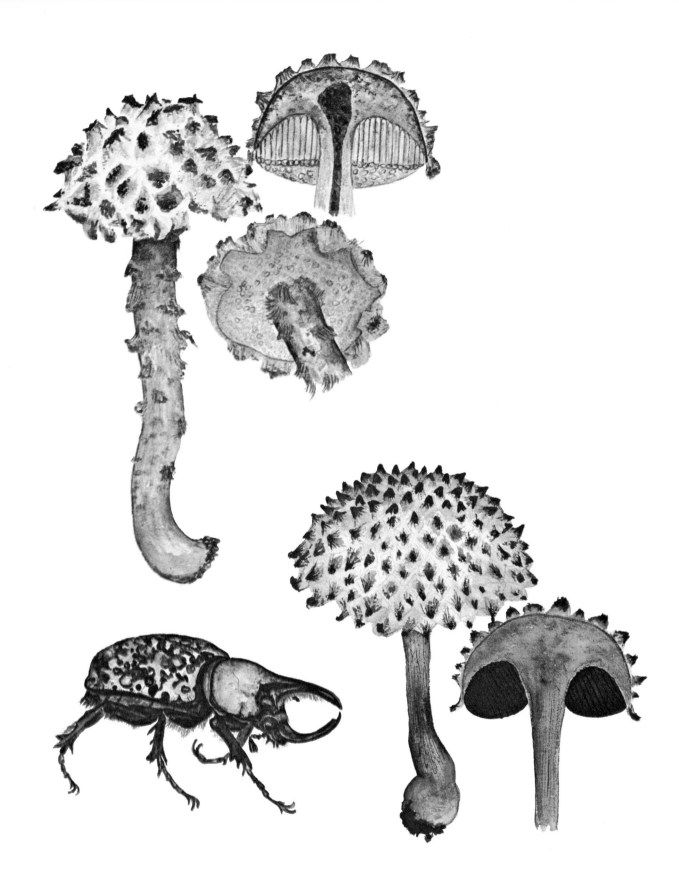

and his attendants were riding across the sky on their horses, when suddenly, they began to be pursued by demons. In order to escape these demons they had to ride their horses very hard. As a result, the horses began to foam at the mouth and to bleed. The blood and foam mixed, and wherever it struck the ground a red fly-agaric with white spots sprang up.

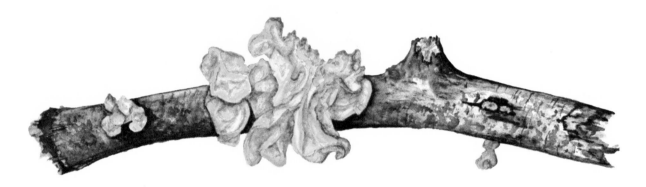

Living organisms called fungi are very complex and diverse. Although a mushroom seems to appear overnight, we know there is a definite developmental period that usually lasts several days. Nutritionally, mushrooms can live on a wide variety of materials.

Some people collect mushrooms simply to eat for their delicate and delicious flavors. Other than the edible varieties, quite a few toxic ones exist, some of which are sought by some people for their hallucinogenic properties.

Finally, we have examined many unusual phenomena which characterize this group of organisms, such as fairy rings, rapid color changes, distinct odors, and bioluminescence. These features have created many myths. We have also demonstrated that many of these myths have a factual basis. Whether fact or folklore, the mushroom's phenomena are unique. Thus, this group of organisms can truly be called a "separate kingdom."

Catalogue of Paintings

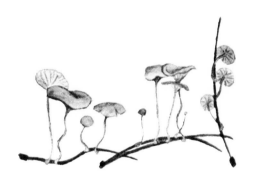

Because these mushrooms were painted on location and due to the extraordinary number and variety of them, some of the mushroom identifications are incomplete.

Bibliography

Buller, A. H. R. 1916. The fungus lore of the Greeks and Romans. TRANSACTIONS BRITISH MYCOLOGICAL SOCIETY. 5: 21-66.

———. 1924. THE PRODUCTION AND LIBERATION OF SPORES IN HYMENOMYCETES AND UREDINEAE. Researches on fungi. Vol. 3. London: Longmans Green & Co.

Dioszegi, V. 1968. POPULAR BELIEFS AND FOLKLORE TRADITION IN SIBERIA. The Hague: Mouton & Co.

Gilmore, M. R. 1911. Uses of plants by the Indians of the Missouri river region. THE ANNUAL REPORT OF THE BUREAU OF AMERICAN ETHNOLOGY. 33: 62.

Houghton, W. 1885. Notices of fungi in Greek and Latin authors. ANNUAL MAGAZINE OF NATURAL HISTORY, ser. 5, 15: 22-49.

Lincoff, G. and Mitchel, D. H. 1977. TOXIC AND HALLUCINOGENIC MUSHROOM POISONING. New York: Van Nostrand Reinhold Co.

McIlvaine, C. 1973. ONE THOUSAND AMERICAN FUNGI. Reprint of 2nd Ed. New York: Dover Publications.

Nelson, E. W. 1896-97. The Eskimo about Bering Strait. THE ANNUAL REPORT OF THE BUREAU OF AMERICAN ETHNOLOGY. 18: 271.

Ramsbotton, J. 1953. MUSHROOMS & TOADSTOOLS. A STUDY OF THE ACTIVITIES OF FUNGI. London: Collins.

Robbins, W. W.; Harrington, J. P.; and Freire-Marreco, B. 1916. The Tewa Indians. BULLETIN OF THE BUREAU OF AMERICAN ETHNOLOGY. 55: 66-67.

Rolfe, R. T. and Rolfe, F. W. 1925. THE ROMANCE OF THE FUNGUS WORLD. London: Chapman & Hall, Ltd.

Shantz, H. L. and Piemeisel, R. L. 1917. Fungus fairy rings in eastern Colorado and their effects on vegetation. JOURNAL OF AGRICULTURAL RESEARCH. 11: 191-245.

Simons, D. M. 1971. The mushroom toxins. DELAWARE MEDICAL JOURNAL. 43(7): 177-187.

Steedman, E. V., ed. 1927-28. Ethnobotany of the Thompson Indians of British Columbia. THE ANNUAL REPORT OF THE BUREAU OF AMERICAN ETHNOLOGY. 45: 483.

Swanton, J. R. 1926. Social and religious beliefs and usages of the Chickasaw Indians. THE ANNUAL REPORT OF THE BUREAU OF AMERICAN ETHNOLOGY. 44: 356.

Wasson, R. G. 1968. SOMA, DIVINE MUSHROOM OF IMMORTALITY. New York: Harcourt, Brace & Jovanovich, Inc.

Wheller, W. M. 1907. THE FUNGUS GROWING ANTS OF NORTH AMERICA. New York: Dover Publications.

MUSHROOMS: A SEPARATE KINGDOM

Text was executed by Loni Parker in an adaptation of Fraktur,
    developed during the German Renaissance.
Color separations by Capitol Engraving Company, Nashville,
    Tennessee.
Textsheets are 80# Warm White Teton by Simpson Paper Company,
    San Francisco, California.
Endleaves are Antique Multi-color Gold by Process Materials
    Corporation, Carlstadt, New Jersey.
Cover cloth is Kingston 3523 Natural Finish by Holliston Mills, Inc.,
    Kingsport, Tennessee.
Printed and bound by Kingsport Press, Kingsport, Tennessee.

First Edition 1979